How to use this book ★ ✦ ★

Follow the advice, in italics, given for you on each page.
Praise *the children at every step!*

Detailed guidance is provided in the Read Write Inc. Phonics Handbook.

7 reading activities

Children:

☆ *Practise reading the speed sounds.*

☆ *Read the green and red words for the Ditty.*

☆ *Listen as you read the introduction.*

☆ *Read the Ditty.*

☆ *Re-read the Ditty and discuss the 'questions to talk about'.*

☆ *Re-read the Ditty with fluency and expression.*

☆ *Practise reading the speed words.*

Speed Sounds

Consonants

Say the pure sounds (do not add 'uh').

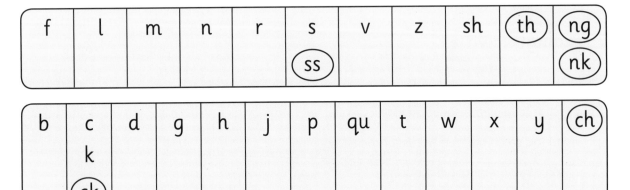

Vowels

Say the sounds in and out of order.

a	e	i	o	u

Each box contains only one sound. Focus sounds are circled.

Ditty 1 # Pick it up

Green words

Read in Fred Talk (pure sounds).

yes   so<u>ck</u>   me<u>ss</u>   vest

p<u>ick</u>   up   <u>th</u>at   it

3

Ditty 1 # Pick it up

Introduction
In this story a boy and his mum tidy up. Who do you think will be messier?

pick up <u>th</u>at so<u>ck</u>

yes

pick up <u>th</u>at vest

yes

pi<u>ck</u> up <u>th</u>at me<u>ss</u>

Ditty 2 Snap snap

Green words

Read in Fred Talk (pure sounds).

six   red   big   snap   in   pi<u>nk</u>

lo<u>ng</u>

Read the root word first and then with the ending.

rat → rats   hat → hats

croc → crocs   so<u>ck</u> → so<u>ck</u>s

Ditty 2   Snap snap

Introduction

This is a story about some rats and some crocodiles. The rats are a bit worried … can you guess why?

six pi<u>nk</u> rats in big red hats

six red crocs in lo<u>ng</u> pi<u>nk</u> so<u>ck</u>s

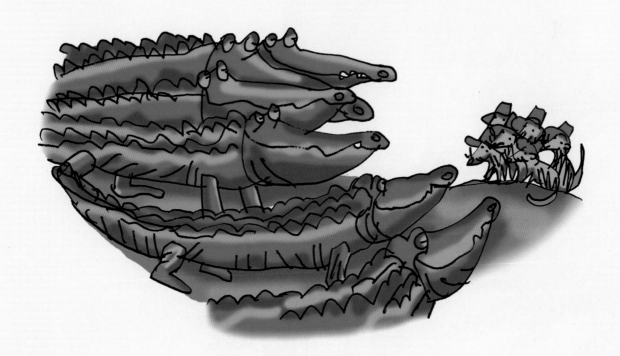

snap snap snap

Ditty 3 # This chimp can run

Green words

Read in Fred Talk (pure sounds).

win   can   <u>th</u>at   run   clap

<u>th</u>is   grin   <u>ch</u>imp

Ditty 3 This chimp can run

Introduction

When you play a game, do you like to win? This is a story about some chimps who are at a sports day. Let's see what they do!

<u>th</u>is <u>ch</u>imp can run

that chimp can grin

this chimp can clap

<u>th</u>at <u>ch</u>imp can win

Questions to talk about

Ditty 1

What does the boy pick up first?

What does the boy say to his mum at the end of the story?

What does your mum/dad/carer ask you to pick up off your bedroom floor?

Ditty 2

How many rats are there?

What are the crocs wearing?

What sort of things do you like dressing up in?

Ditty 3

What can the first chimp do?

What three things can the other chimps do?

Why is this chimp so clever?

Speed words for **Ditty 1**

Children practise reading the words across the rows, down the columns and in and out of order clearly and quickly.

me<u>ss</u>	so<u>ck</u>	yes	pi<u>ck</u>
up	<u>th</u>at	vest	it

Speed words for **Ditty 2**

six	red	big	rat
so<u>ck</u>	in	hat	pi<u>nk</u>

Speed words for **Ditty 3**

win	can	<u>th</u>at	run
<u>th</u>is	grin	can	clap